Glow-worms

John Tyler

Published in Great Britain by
Tyler–Scagell
Tadorna
Bradbourne Vale Road
Sevenoaks
Kent TN13 3DH

ISBN 0 9523526 0 5

Editing and production
Robin Scagell

Printed by
Herald Press, Stratford-upon-Avon

Picture credits

All photographs by John Tyler, except as follows:

Figure 1, Figure 17, back cover: Robin Scagell
Figure 9b: Ernest Trice
Figure 20 is based on an artwork by Hans Schwalb.

Cover: A female glow-worm on a grass stem. As she moves her glowing tail segments from side to side she leaves a trail on the time exposure.

Back cover: The light from this female glow-worm shines on the foliage around her.

CONTENTS

The glow-worm's life-cycle

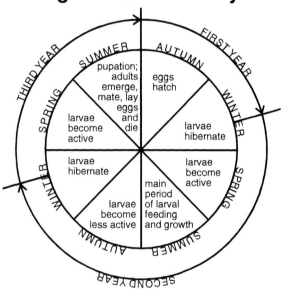

Chapter 1
What is a glow-worm?

Walk along an unlit country lane on a summer night and with luck you may come across small points of vivid green light shining amid the grass. These are glow-worms. The name is misleading, though: they are not worms at all but beetles, which can be distinguished from other types of insect by the fact that most species have a pair of thick wing-cases that close over the insect's back to protect the wings. These wing-cases are unique to beetles and can be seen clearly, for example, on ladybirds.

The glow-worm belongs to a family of beetles known as the *Lampyridae* or fireflies (this is another confusing name, as they are certainly not flies, either!). The fireflies are a huge group containing over 2000 species, with new ones being discovered all the time. The females of many species have more or less stunted wings and wing-cases, whereas the males are normally good flyers and still have the characteristic beetle wing-cases.

The feature which makes fireflies and glow-worms so appealing to even the most casual observer, and the one which earns them their name, is their ability to produce an often dazzling display of light. To stumble upon a cluster of a hundred or more glow-worms displaying is like looking down on the streetlights of a miniature town (though it is an increasingly rare sight nowadays), and in the tropics some species of firefly gather in their thou-

Figure 1. A hillside in Oxfordshire covered with glow-worms.

Figure 2. Fireflies on the Serpentine? Arthur Rackham's illustration from Peter Pan.

thought that the predatory female can distinguish between the signals of several different species, and send the appropriate reply to each one.

The fireflies are an extremely varied group. Some, for example, have larvae which can live (and glow) underwater, and one Jamaican species, *Photinus synchronans*, is even said to avoid predators by mimicking lizard droppings! Another species, *Lamprophorus tenebrosus*, has been known to take care of her eggs until they hatch, a rare thing among insects, which normally abandon them as soon as they are laid. She will stand guard over her clutch of eggs and gather them up if they become scattered.

The firefly's almost magical light has attracted human attention for generations. It is described in an ancient Chinese encyclopaedia written over 2000 years ago by a pupil of Confucius. They often featured in Japanese folk medicine, and in 13th Century Arabia fireflies were crushed, mixed with attar of roses and dripped into the ear as a treatment for suppuration. All over the world they have been the inspiration for countless poems, paintings and stories. Here in Britain, for example, there are plenty of anecdotes describing how glow-worms have been used to read by or as emergency bicycle lamps when a cyclist's batteries have failed without warning. Early travellers in the New World came back with similar stories, of how the native people of Central America would collect luminous cucujo beetles (a type of click beetle) and release them indoors to light up their huts.

sands to form walls of lights, all flashing on and off in synchronism. The light is used by the adult fireflies as a signal to attract a mate, and each species must develop its own 'call-sign' to avoid being confused with other species glowing nearby. So within any one area each species will differ from its neighbours in some way, for example in the colour or pattern of its light, how long the pulses of light last, the interval between pulses and whether it displays in flight or from the ground.

However, at least one firefly has been able to crack the code and make the signals of other species work to its advantage. The female *Photuris versicolor*, an American species, can impersonate the female of another firefly called *Photinus* by mimicking the pattern of flashes that a genuine *Photinus* would use to attract a male. When a hopeful male *Photinus* arrives expecting to find a mate, the female *Photuris* turns on him and eats him. It is

Girls threaded them around their feet to light up the forest paths at night.

Fireflies very similar to those we see today have been found fossilised in rocks which were formed about 30 million years ago, and their ancestors were probably glowing long before then. The species found today in North and South America are quite distinct from those which live in Europe and Asia, suggesting that the ancestors of the two groups parted company a very long time ago and have remained largely isolated from each other ever since, each evolving in their own direction.

It is impossible to be sure exactly when and where the first firefly appeared. The highest concentrations of firefly species today are to be found in the tropics of South America, which may mean either that this is where they first evolved, or simply that they prefer the conditions there.

Wherever they first arose, fireflies have since spread to almost every part of the globe. They may have travelled by sea, on flotsam carried along by ocean currents, or on foot, at a time when South America was still connected to Africa, Antarctica and Australia. Today members of the firefly family can be found almost anywhere outside the Arctic and Antarctic circles, from Tierra del Fuego in the south to Sweden in the north.

Britain is perched on the northern edge of the area in which fireflies can survive, and so we have just two species (compare this to Jamaica for example, where about 50 species live in a country about 20 times smaller that the British Isles). One of them, *Phosphaenus hemipterus*, is sometimes known as the little glow-worm, being the smaller of the two (the male is about 6 to 8 mm in length and the female about 10 mm). Very little is known about *Phosphaenus*, but it is said to be active during the day and the adults of both sexes are only weakly luminous. Perhaps its one claim to fame is that it seems to be the only known firefly species in which neither the male nor the female can fly. The female has no wings at all and the male's are too small to be of any use. They are covered by equally tiny wing-cases which make him look as if he is wearing a waistcoat.

Phosphaenus can be found in Europe, though it seems to be relatively rare (or perhaps just overlooked) wherever it occurs. There are records of it from as far afield as Newfoundland, but it has probably been carried there by accident, perhaps in the ballast of ships. In Britain it seems to have been restricted to a small area of south-east England, and even there it has not been recorded for some years, so it may now be extinct in this country.

The other species, and the only one which most of us are ever likely to see in Britain, is the common or European glow-worm, *Lampyris noctiluca*, which is widespread and relatively abundant. This is the species on which I will concentrate in this book.

Chapter 2
The glow-worm's life

When people talk of seeing a glow-worm they normally mean the brightly glowing adult female. This is certainly the most conspicuous stage of the life cycle, but in fact it makes up no more than two per cent of her lifespan.

As with many insects the glow-worm's life is divided into four distinct stages: the egg, the larva (equivalent to the caterpillar of a butterfly), the pupa (or chrysalis) and the adult.

The egg

The glow-worm begins its life in the autumn as a pale yellow egg, roughly spherical and about a millimetre across (Figure 3a). The freshly laid egg is extremely fragile and would burst at the slightest touch, but within a day its surface has hardened into a shell. For the first few days it may glow with a very faint yellow light, which seems to come either from the yolk of the egg itself or from a thin coating of 'glue' which the mother used to stick the egg in position. The egg usually takes about 35 days to hatch, but the exact time varies according to the temperature, from about 27 days in hot weather to more than 45 days in cold weather. At first the egg appears to be a featureless milky mass, but by the time it is due to hatch the segments of the young glow-worm can be seen pressed tightly against the inside of the shell, with its body arched over and its head touching its tail (Figure 3b). By now the larva's light organ is fully developed, and its glow signals that the egg will soon hatch.

The newly hatched larva

Once it is ready to leave the egg the larva presses its body against the sides until the shell bursts open, and then climbs out. When it first emerges the larva is about 5 mm long and has soft, smoky grey skin, but within a few hours this has hardened and darkened until it is virtually black. Seen from above the larva is made up of a head followed by 12 body segments, each with two yellow spots at the hind corners (Figure 4). At this stage there is no obvious difference between males and females, but from studies of larvae reared in captivity it seems that the two sexes are born in roughly equal numbers. Although its size will increase enormously over the next year or so the larva's overall appearance will hardly change at all until it is ready to become an adult: a large larva simply looks like a scaled-up version of a small one (Figure 5).

The snail-eater

In many insects the larval and adult stages of the life cycle have become specialised for different tasks, and this is certainly true of the glow-worm. The larva devotes much of its life to feeding and building up its food reserves so that as an adult it will be free to concentrate all its efforts on the task of finding a mate and reproducing. The young glow-worm has quite a specialised diet. Like many other firefly species it feeds almost exclusively on snails and slugs, and over millions of years of evolution its body and its

Figure 3. Glow-worm eggs, newly laid (a, left) and a few days before hatching (b, right). The eggs are usually hidden from sight under stones or vegetation

behaviour have become beautifully adapted to hunting, killing and eating them.

After a few hours' rest to allow its skin to harden, the young larva is ready to begin the search for its first snail. This may mean several days of marching on an empty stomach, but a typical larva can comfortably maintain a pace of about five metres an hour. This may not sound much, even compared to a snail, but kept up non-stop it would allow the larva to search 120 metres in a day.

Figure 4. Newly hatched larvae. These have already taken on their characteristic dark colour, but when they emerge from the egg they are much paler in colour.

Figure 5. Glow-worm larvae, fully grown (left) and young (right).

Finding a meal

The larva improves its chances of finding snails by concentrating on their favourite habitats. One of the few people to study the sorts of conditions that the glow-worm larva looks for was Hans Schwalb, a German researcher, who found that its preferences are very similar to those of the snail. For example, studies of captive larvae suggest that the larva is most active at night, when snails do most of their feeding. Captive larvae which were allowed to choose from a range of different light intensities usually opted for complete darkness. They appeared to ignore red light, though, so fitting a red filter to a torch is a useful way of studying them at night. Captive larvae also showed a preference for moist conditions, again like snails. Given a choice between wet and dry sand they usually chose the wet, and if they were allowed to choose between different degrees of humidity they usu-

ally went for 100 per cent relative humidity. In fact, glow-worm larvae are particularly sensitive to drying out, and at a relative humidity of about 45 per cent most die through loss of water within a matter of hours. Glow-worm larvae also resemble snails in avoiding very hot conditions. Schwalb found that captive larvae which were allowed to wander along a gradient of temperatures, from the boiling point to the freezing point of water, never willingly went above 40°C.

Because it is largely nocturnal, sight is of very little use to a hunting glow-worm. Even when it is about during the day the larva usually keeps low in the vegetation, where lighting and visibility are often poor. Each of its eyes consists of just a single black facet which detects movement and changes in brightness rather than forming an image as our eyes do, so it certainly could not spot a snail at any great distance. But the larva makes up for its short-sightedness by using its stubby

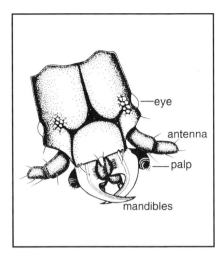

Figure 6. The larva's head, seen from above (left) and below (right)

antennae, together with six extremely sensitive feelers (called palps) around its mouth, to explore the ground in front of it. Whenever the larva is walking its palps can be seen constantly waving about, stretching out to touch or taste anything in its path. They seem to be the young glow-worm's main point of contact with the outside world, and it often appears to be totally oblivious of anything going on even a few centimetres away.

It is not clear whether the larva just stumbles upon its meals or whether it can actually follow the trail of mucus left by a snail. Larvae in captivity do sometimes seem to be attracted to surfaces over which snails have wandered, but at other times a larva will walk straight across the trail left by a snail just seconds earlier. But whether it finds its prey by luck or judgement, sooner or later the larva will come face to face with a snail, and then it must tackle a tricky problem: somehow it must overcome a creature which is often more than 15 times its own weight – the equivalent of a child taking on a grizzly bear. And if they meet on a grass stem and the glow-worm attacks too clumsily the snail will just pull itself into its shell, fall to the ground and escape. So, not surprisingly, the larva normally approaches the snail with great stealth and explores its skin very cautiously before delivering the first bite.

The kill

The larva's jaws (or mandibles) are sharp and sickle-shaped, curving inwards to meet in front of the mouth. Each has a narrow tube running down its length and opening near the tip (Figure 6). The larva gives the snail's foot a series of gentle nips, quickly drawing in its head after each one. The head is much smaller than the segment immediately behind it (which extends forward like a hood) and is mounted on a long flexible neck so that it can be quickly pulled into the hood at the first sign of danger. As it does so the

11

Figure 7. A larva riding a snail.

larva's eye becomes covered by a fold of skin, which seems to act rather like an eyelid, wiping the eye clean and protecting it from knocks and scratches.

It takes less than a second to deliver each bite, but each time the jaws pierce the skin a small amount of brown toxic fluid is pumped down the hollow mandibles and into the snail's body. The poison is produced in the larva's intestine and is able to digest proteins. The number of bites that the larva needs to overcome the snail depends on their relative sizes: a single bite from a well-grown larva may be enough to halt a snail about a centimetre across, but it may need to bite larger ones ten times or more.

While it is waiting for the poison to take effect the young glow-worm will often ride on the snail's shell (Figure 7), but it is always careful not to set foot directly onto the mucus-covered skin. From time to time the larva will clamber to the entrance of the shell and put its head round the corner, apparently checking whether the meal is ready. Slugs of course do not have this convenient platform and so they have to be worked on from ground level (Figure 8).

At first the snail may try to defend itself by covering its body with a thick lather of mucus froth and the larva has to be careful not to get its legs or antennae stuck. No matter how cautious the glow-worm is, accidents will happen and larvae often become glued to their snail, or else find it difficult to release their grip after a bite and end up trying to break free by towing the snail along backwards. But as the poison

begins to act on the snail's nerves and muscles the victim first becomes paralysed and is then slowly digested into a 'broth' which the larva can lap up. It has a sieve of hairs inside its mouth which it uses to strain off any lumps of flesh which are still too large to swallow, and a pair of pointed blades on the inside edges of its mandibles to break them into more manageable pieces. As it feeds, the larva pours more poison directly through its mouth to speed up the digestion.

Throughout most of the meal the snail is paralysed but still alive. Its heart rate, which rose rapidly after the first bite, now begins to fall as the poison takes effect, but is still going as much as 16 hours later. In fact in some cases the partly eaten snail has then been known to recover and crawl away!

In captivity, larvae will often feed in a pack, with as many as 15 of them gathered around the shell of a single paralysed snail, but in the wild larvae are likely to be spread out much more

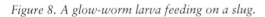

Figure 8. A glow-worm larva feeding on a slug.

Figure 9. (a, left): The larva's tail organ, seen from above.
(b): A close-up of the tentacle hooks.

thinly, so sharing their meals in this way is probably a very rare event.

Having a wash

Feeding is a slow and messy business for a glow-worm and the larva often pauses to wander off a little way for a rest and a wash before returning to its meal. To clean off the mucus and partly digested flesh the glow-worm has evolved an extremely versatile little device at the tip of its abdomen. The tail organ is made up of a cluster of branching, cream-coloured tentacles (Figure 9a). Each of these is armed with several hundred backward-pointing hooks, less than a hundredth of a millimetre in length and arranged in neat rows across the tentacle (Figure 9b). When not in use the organ can be turned inside out and stored away inside the larva's tail. The glow-worm uses it as a scouring pad, painstakingly wiping down every joint and segment of its body and paying particular attention to its face.

As well as being extremely useful for personal hygiene the tail organ has two other uses. First, as it walks along the larva repeatedly curls its tail under its body, uses the tail organ to anchor itself to the ground and then straightens its tail to push itself forward (it can also be used in reverse to pull the larva out of the slimy mess of a half-digested snail). Second, in its travels the larva sometimes wanders up plant stems or over stones, and if it loses its footing while climbing the grip of the tail organ is strong enough, at least in small larvae, to take the full weight of its body. The larva, hanging by its tail, can then swing from side to side until its claws are able to find a new foothold.

The grip of the glow-worm's tail organ appears to work on the same two principles as a fly's foot. On soft or uneven surfaces, such as soil or plants, it uses the rows of hooks to cling on. But on much smoother surfaces like stone it relies on capillary action, in which a thin film of liquid on each tentacle binds it to the ground (tiny drops of this liquid can occasionally be seen if a larva is allowed to walk over a sheet of glass).

The menu

Although very little has been written about their food preferences in the wild, in captivity larvae do not seem particularly choosy about which snail species they will tackle. All of the species shown in the table below have been eaten in captivity.

The larva's tastes may change as it gets older. For example, a fully grown banded snail makes a good meal for a large larva, but might be too big to be killed by a newly hatched one. On the other hand the large larva would find it almost impossible to get at a small species such as the rounded snail once it had retreated into its shell.

A change of clothes

Because each snail can be many times larger than the glow-worm itself, the larva's body must be able to carry large quantities of food. This is processed into fat and then stored in hundreds of round fat-bodies, which in a well fed larva fill almost the whole body cavity, from head to tail. Each

Table 1: Snails eaten in captivity.

Scientific name	English name
Aegopinella nitidula	Smooth snail
Arianta arbustorum	Copse snail
Arion ater	Black slug
Arion circumscriptus	Slug
Arion hortensis	Slug
Arion subfuscus	Slug
Cepaea hortensis	White-lipped banded snail
Deroceras reticulatum	Slug
Discus rotundatus	Rounded snail
Ena obscura	Lesser bulin
Helicella itala	Heath snail
Helicella obvia	Snail
Helicopsis striata	Snail
Helix aspersa	Garden snail
Helix pomatia	Roman snail
Isognomostoma isognomostoma	Snail
Monacha cantiana	Kentish snail*
Oxychilus alliarius	Garlic snail
Oxychilus cellarius	Cellar snail
Trichia hispida	Hairy snail*
Vitrea crystallina	Crystal snail
Zebrina detrita	Snail

* These species are also known to be eaten in the wild.

fat-body is about a fifth of a millimetre across and may be pale yellow or pink, depending upon where it is in the body.

Each segment of the larva's body is made up of rigid plates on the upper, lower and side surfaces. These are brownish black in colour and act rather like plates of armour, strong enough to support the larva's body and protect it from injury, but largely unable to stretch or bend as the larva grows. On the other hand the skin between the plates, which is a pale cream colour, is far more flexible and elastic. In an unfed larva it is folded into deep creases, so that the rigid plates are almost touching in places, but as the larva feeds the skin both unfolds and stretches, allowing the body's volume to increase dramatically. The larva also has bands of this flexible skin between one segment and the next, and between the left and right halves of the upper plate, which spread apart so that it can expand still further. When this happens a pale yellow line of soft skin appears down the centre of the back: the mark of a well-fed larva (Figure 10).

But the flexibility of the glow-worm's skin eventually reaches a limit and then the larva must shed its old skin and replace it with a larger size. The new skin forms beneath the old one, which then becomes detached and splits open along a built-in line of weakness, allowing the larva to climb free. In many beetles this line of weakness runs down the centre of the back, but for some reason in the glow-worm it forms along the edges of the front segments. The larva, often lying on its back, emerges head-first and discards the old skin rather like someone trying to climb out of a sleeping bag by a

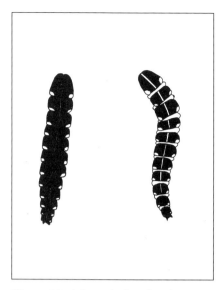

Figure 10. A larva before feeeding (left) and after (right).

combination of wriggling, arching its body and alternately expanding and contracting each segment. Several of the larva's body segments have a pair of large backward-pointing bristles on the underside and these may act as spikes or ratchets to push the old skin away.

Moulting can be a slow process, often taking several hours or even a day to complete. When the newly clothed larva does finally emerge, it is extremely fragile and would be easy prey for predators such as ground beetles, but after a few hours in the air the skin has hardened and assumed its characteristic black colour. In the course of its life the young glow-worm will moult several times (no-one is yet sure of the exact number but it may be about five for males, and possibly more for females).

Moulting is often brought on by a large meal, which stretches the skin to its limit, and the larva sometimes protects itself at this vulnerable stage by moulting inside the shell which it has just emptied. But even if it avoids being eaten by predators, moulting is a hazardous operation and larvae often die or become disfigured if they are unable to shed their old skin successfully. In some cases part of the old skin may become lodged around the new one, preventing it from expanding as the larva tries to grow. In other cases a patch of the old skin may actually fuse with the new one, so that although the larva can moult, it has to keep the moulted skin attached to its body. In one adult female that I saw this problem seems to have repeated itself at the next moult as well, forcing her to carry around the skins of both the larva and the pupa.

Flashing lights

The glow-worm larva is able to produce a yellow-green light from a pair of organs on the underside of its body, near the tip of its abdomen, and although this light is much fainter than the female's, on a dark night it can be seen more than five metres away. The larva appears to use its light in at least three different ways, two of which seem to have straightforward explanations, while the third is more puzzling.

First, if the larva is disturbed, for example by handling or a vibration, it will sometimes switch on its lights for a few seconds and then turn them off again. It seems quite likely that this is just a defensive reaction, intended to scare off a would-be predator.

Second, some larvae have been known to glow continuously for hours at a time without any apparent provocation. These are often fully grown larvae which will soon be pupating, so it might be that this glow, which is very much like the adult female's, is just part of the preparation for adulthood, at a time when the larva's body is undergoing all sorts of internal changes.

These two types of glowing can also be seen in adult glow-worms, but the third type seems to be unique to the larva. As it walks along it sometimes produces distinct pulses of light, each one normally lasting a few seconds and consisting of a period of a second or so while the brightness builds up, followed by a period of steady brightness and then a final period during which the light fades and goes out altogether. Each of these pulses is separated from the next by a longer interval of darkness lasting several seconds, creating an effect rather like a miniature lighthouse.

This is the larval display which is most often seen in the wild and sometimes leads to the larva being mistaken for an adult female, but it can be distinguished from the adult in at least three ways: (1) the spot of light appears much smaller and fainter than the female's, (2) the light is often produced while the larva is on the move, whereas females are nearly always stationary, and (3) the light comes in pulses rather than the steady glow of the female. This pulsing of the light often gives people the impression that the glow-worm has switched off its light because they have disturbed it, whereas in fact the larva is probably completely unaware of them and will light up again a few seconds later.

Unlike the other two types of glowing, which the larva seems to be able to do at almost any time (though of course it is only noticeable in the dark), the larva normally only starts this 'lighthouse' display once the sky around it has reached a certain darkness. This light threshold may be the reason why larvae often fail to glow on bright moonlit nights, and it may also explain why glowing larvae are less often seen in midsummer, when evenings stay relatively light, whereas after about the end of August sightings become much more common.

A mystery

Several authors have exercised their imaginations by trying to suggest reasons for the larva's curious display, but so far none of them can really be said to have been proven. Here are a few of the most commonly offered explanations:

First, it is possible that the larva's glow has no purpose at all and is just a by-product of the light organs which are developing inside it, ready to be used in the adult female. So far no-one knows for sure whether both male and female larvae glow, but if they do then this explanation would be seriously weakened because adult males do very little glowing. It also fails to explain why the larval light is pulsed, rather than constant like the female's. The other problem is that, as we will see later, the two larval light spots make up just a small portion of the light organ in the adult female. The rest of it does not appear until she pupates, so why must these two spots be switched on several months earlier? It also seems a waste of energy to keep producing light which you don't need.

It has also been suggested that the larva's light is used as a torch to light its way at night, but if this is so then why does it keep switching it on and off, and why does it carry it at the rear, where it lights up where it has come from rather than where it is going? In any case we have already seen that the larva has very poor eyesight and relies much more on touch to find its way around.

Another suggestion is that the larva uses its light as a lure to attract its prey. Apart from the fact that there is little or no evidence to suggest that snails are actually attracted to light, it seems odd that the larva should make it more difficult for the snail by continuing to move along as it glows.

A fourth possibility is that the light is a signal to other larvae, either calling them in to share a meal or warning them off to avoid overcrowding. The larvae of other firefly species have been found sharing snails in the wild, but our larva gives its performance whether it has found a snail or not. And the glow-worm's poor eyesight, together with the low visibility of its habitat, would probably mean that it would have to come within half a metre or less before it could see the signal, which would not be of much help in preventing overcrowding.

Perhaps more plausible is the idea that by sending out pulses of light every so often the larva is deterring potential predators. This is after all what it does when it is actually attacked, and by using pulses rather than a constant glow it would make it more difficult for the predator to locate (it certainly works for humans trying to find larvae in the dark!). This tactic may not work for invertebrate predators such as spiders and centipedes, whose eyesight is as bad as the glow-worm's, but it may help to scare and confuse creatures like shrews and woodmice.

A similar possibility is that the larva is actually protected by unpleasant-tasting, or even poisonous, chemicals in its body, and that its light is meant not just to scare predators off but to warn them that if they do attack they might regret it. Many insects which are active during the day, such as ladybirds and some moths and caterpillars, use bright colours and striking patterns to advertise the fact that they taste revolting. Once a predator has tried a few and learnt to associate the markings with the taste it is unlikely to make the same mistake again. Bright colours would obviously be of very little use to a nocturnal insect like the glow-worm larva, so it may have chosen light instead. There are certainly reports of birds, lizards and even ants refusing to eat fireflies, but as yet no-one seems to have looked (or tasted) to see whether they contain any unpleasant compounds.

At the moment it is impossible to tell which, if any, of these explanations is the correct one. Of course it is just possible that they all are!

The larva's calendar

Almost nothing is known about how quickly the glow-worm larva grows in the wild, but if captive ones are anything to go by, its life seems to consist of a short spurt of growth sandwiched between two long and relatively static spells during which it feeds very little and does not change very much in size.

A typical pattern might be as follows. During the autumn of its first year, if there are enough snails about, the larva will probably be able to put on enough weight to moult once or twice. But then as winter sets in it becomes more and more lethargic and eventually goes into a sort of hibernation. This makes good sense, as snails become increasingly hard to find in winter and those that do survive often seal themselves into their shells with a strong sheet of dried mucus, which makes them virtually glow-worm-proof. Larvae often spend the winter under logs, stones or leaf litter, their bodies drawn in like concertinas, with the rear half of each segment overlapping the front half of the one behind it.

I have even found larvae hibernating in the hollow cores of tree stumps in the middle of a reedbed. Nearby, another larva was passing the winter in the centre of a reedmace stem, where it had adopted a tunnel bored out and abandoned by a bulrush moth caterpillar. The tree stumps and the reeds were surrounded on all sides by water, so the larvae must have been feeding in the reedbed during the previous summer, when it had largely dried out, and then retreated upwards as the water level began to rise in late autumn. They would be marooned there until the water receded again the following spring.

In the spring of their second year, when the larvae wake from their 'sleep', some are not much larger than they were when they first hatched, but then they get down to the business of eating in earnest. Although a larva may live for 15 months or more, most of its growth will be crammed into the next five months or so, and some larvae will put on so much weight during this time that they will need to shed their skins twice in one month. The female larvae grow much more rapidly than the males and by the end of August they can be recognised by their larger size, even though it will be another nine months or more before they become adults. By about the end of

September the growth spurt will be coming to an end and the larva will stop moulting, lose its appetite and become less active, preparing to sleep through its second winter. The larva begins to feed again in the spring of its third year, but by now it is already nearly full-grown and may not need to moult again before it pupates.

A typical larva's growth is summarised in Figure 11, which shows the average size of 24 larvae reared in captivity and illustrates clearly both the growth spurt and the difference in the rates of growth of males and females. It is important to remember, though, that in the wild, where conditions and the availability of snails can be quite different, the larva's growth rate and the precise timing of its moults may also vary. The length of a glow-worm's body is a very poor indicator of its overall size because the larva expands and contracts as it moves, so the measurement used in Figure 11 is the width of the pronotum, the large 'hood' at the front of its body. This is relatively rigid and so gives a much more consistent measure of size. The width of the pronotum can also provide a useful guide to the sex of the larva: if it measures less than about 4 mm then the larva could be either a male or a young female, but if it is 4 mm or more then the larva is likely to be a female.

Only a small proportion of larvae will survive the full 15 months or so. Many will have been eaten by predators, or succumbed to fungal infections or dehydration, so that on average only about two larvae from the original brood of 50–100 will live long enough to reproduce two years later. It

Figure 11. Pronotum sizes of growing larvae, shown actual size.

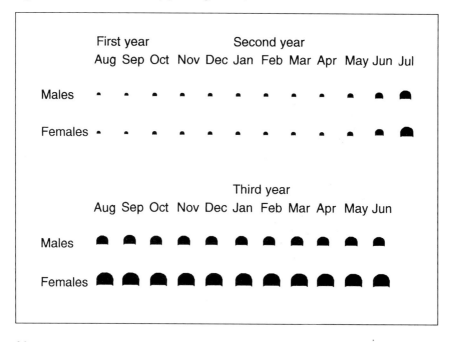

also seems that some larvae may need an extra year before they are ready to pupate, but it is not yet clear how commonly this happens.

In early summer the larvae which are ready to pupate that year seem to shake off their nocturnal habits and can often be seen striding purposefully along in broad daylight. As we shall see, the adult female rarely moves far before she dies, so it may be that this final larval stage is the one in which glow-worms are able to spread out in search of new habitats.

When it has finished its walkabout and is ready to begin the transformation into an adult the larva usually searches for some form of cover such as a log. Larvae preparing to pupate often gather together in small groups, and it is fairly common to find six or more side by side under one log. It is possible that they gang together in this way by producing a scent to attract other larvae, or each larva may simply wander from log to log until it stumbles upon another one and then stays

with it. However they do it, this 'ganging' makes good sense as it saves a lot of time and travelling when the adults emerge and start looking for a mate.

The pupa

Many firefly species prepare for pupation by digging into the ground to create a small chamber, but the glow-worm does not bother with this and instead just curls up and lies motionless, normally on its back or its side, for a few days until it is ready to shed the last of its larval skins. As with the other larval moults a split forms across the front edge of the thorax and along the sides of the first three segments. Sometimes the pupa frees itself from the old skin by turning on to its front and wriggling away from it, but more often it just lies on its back and expands, contracts and wriggles its abdomen until the crumpled skin has been pushed up to the tip of the tail and can be shaken off (Figure 12). As it is shedding the larval skin the pupa excretes a

Figure 12. A female pupa shedding its final larval skin.

Figure 13. Glow-worm pupae. Note the difference in size and the developing wings and wing-cases of the male (right).

drop of clear liquid, which often remains balanced on the tip of its tail for several hours or even days.

The pupa's skin is extremely thin and translucent, with none of the armour-plating of the larva, and through it can be seen the beginnings of the adult structures. At first the areas which are to become the hard parts, such as the legs and toughened plates, are a pale yellow colour, in contrast to the soft skin between them which is pink, but after a few hours the whole pupa becomes a more uniform olive green.

During the pupal stage most of the organs of the larva's body are completely broken down, to be replaced by the adult versions. Among the few organs which escape this fate are the twin spots of the larval light organ, which remain visible through the pupa's skin and will be passed on to the adult. The pupa will often glow in response to handling or a vibration, but will also light up for no apparent reason. It will also wriggle about quite violently if exposed to bright sunlight. The male pupa can easily be distinguished from the female by his smaller size and by his narrow strap-like wings, which are lacking in the female (Figure 13).

Compared to the months spent as a larva, the pupal stage is quite brief, lasting about 8-12 days for a female and 11-15 days for a male. As we shall see later, the transformation from larva to adult seems to involve rather more drastic structural changes for the male than it does for the female, and this may be the reason for him taking a few days longer than her to complete the change.

The adult female

Female glow-worms often appear a few days before the first male. In most years this happens in June or July, though the precise date varies from year to year and from site to site. In some years it is possible to find the odd one as early as May or as late as October.

The adult female bears a striking resemblance to the larva. She too has a segmented body and no wings or wing cases, but she can be recognised by the lack of pale spots at the hind corners of each segment. A pale line of un-pigmented skin runs down the centre of her back, through which her long tubular heart can be seen beating once every couple of seconds or so, the pulse travelling up the body from tail to head. She has no proper jaws because she does not need to eat: she will live entirely on the food reserves which she built up as a larva. This makes her life something of a race against time, in which she must attract a male, mate with him and lay her eggs before her energy supply runs out.

The glow-worm's glow

It is the female's light which has earnt the species its name, and the structure of the light organ is probably the most thoroughly studied aspect of the glow-worm's biology. It is set on the underside of the body, towards the tip of the abdomen, and consists of large luminous bands on both the sixth and seventh segments and a luminous spot on either side of the eighth segment (Figure 14). (There are occasional oddities, such as females with an extra spot or two on the fifth segment, but these are rare.) The spots on the eighth segment

Figure 14. The spots and bands of the female light organ.

are those which first developed in the larva and were glowing even before it hatched from the egg, but the two main luminous patches on the sixth and seventh segments were formed much later, once the larva had reached maturity.

Starting from the undersurface and working towards the interior of the body, each light organ is made up of three layers (Figure 15), whose functions correspond roughly to the glass, light bulb and reflector of a torch. First there is a transparent window of toughened skin, through which the light shines; then the glowing layer itself, which is made up of large light-emitting cells; and finally a layer of cells packed with crystals of uric acid which act as mirrors, reflecting light back through the window (it is the crystals in the reflector layer which give the underside of the female's tail its pale colour when seen in daylight).

Cold light

The glow-worm's light, like that of all fireflies, is produced by a string of chemical reactions. The central players in these are two compounds with very similar names but very different structures: luciferin and luciferase. Luciferin is a fairly small molecule by biological standards, consisting of just three rings of atoms (Figure 16a). Not all of the details of the light-producing reaction have been worked out, but it appears to involve building up the luciferin molecule's energy and then allowing it to fall apart again, releasing that energy as light. First, oxygen and another molecule called adenosine triphosphate (ATP) are attached to the luciferin molecule, making it more energetic and less stable. This causes the luciferin to throw off some of its atoms, releasing energy in the form of light.

The luciferin molecule is completely dwarfed by its partner, luciferase.

Whereas luciferin contains just a couple of dozen atoms, luciferase is made up of over 10,000. It is an enzyme, a protein consisting of a single chain of carbon and nitrogen atoms with other groups of atoms branching off to either side (Figure 16b). The chain is coiled up on itself, not randomly like tangling up a piece of string, but in a very precise and controlled way, giving each luciferase molecule the same three-dimensional shape.

The role of luciferase in the light-producing reaction is as a catalyst, bringing the various molecules together and holding them in the correct positions while they react with each other. Unlike the other molecules, luciferase is not used up in the process, and once the reaction is complete it can let go of the spent molecules and move on to gather a fresh set.

The instructions for making luciferase are carried by the glow-worm's genes, which specify such things as the number of atoms in the main chain and the type of side branches which they carry. Millions of years of evolution mean that each firefly species now carries its own form of the luciferase gene. It is the structure of the luciferase, rather than the luciferin, which determines the colour of a firefly's light, and a change to just a few per cent of the gene is enough to change the colour of the light. Different individuals of the same species may carry slightly different versions of the luciferase gene and so produce slightly different colours, and some species may even use different luciferases in different parts of their bodies (for example the luminous click-beetle *Pyrophorus lagiophthalmus* often has green headlamps and orange tail-lights).

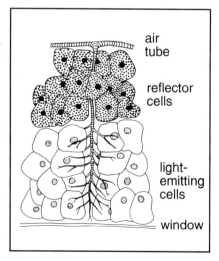

air
tube

reflector
cells

light-
emitting
cells

window

Figure 15. A diagrammatic section through the female light organ.

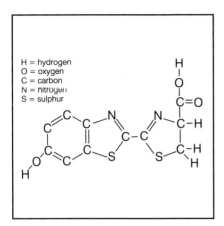

Figure 16a. The structure of luciferin –
a small molecule.

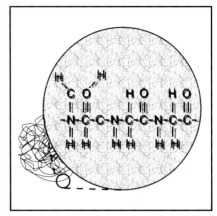

Figure 16b. Luciferase (one fragment
shown in detail) is much larger.

The luciferin–luciferase reaction is used to produce light in a wide range of distantly related groups such as flies, jellyfish, bacteria and fungi. Many luminous groups contain non-luminous species, and vice versa. It may be that the genes controlling the reaction have evolved independently in each group, but it seems more likely that they first appeared over a thousand million years ago in the common ancestor of all these groups and have subsequently been switched off in species and groups which no longer need them. If this is the case then the light-producing genes are probably lying dormant in many non-luminous species, including ourselves.

Incidentally, firefly luciferase has also proved very useful in medical and biological research, where the luciferase gene can be attached to other genes, 'lighting up' to indicate when those genes are active in a plant or animal. Luciferase can also be used to search for life on other planets, because it is able to detect minute amounts of ATP, which is found in every living species (at least on Earth).

The reaction of luciferin and luciferase produces a yellow-green light which covers the region of the spectrum to which the human eye is most sensitive, making it visible many metres away. The reaction is extremely efficient, wasting less than 2 per cent of its energy as heat, compared with about 96 per cent in a typical electric light bulb, so a brilliantly glowing female feels completely cold to the touch. The oxygen needed for the reaction is carried to the light organ by a network of branching air tubes running from a pore on either side of each segment. In fact, provided that enough oxygen is reaching the light organ it can continue to glow even after death: one female which was accidentally trodden on and crushed was still glowing several hours later. The female appears to be able to control the bands and spots of her light organ independently of each other, often flashing her sidelights when disturbed and only switching to full-beam when trying to attract a mate.

The performance

The female usually begins to glow soon after dusk, which during the season is generally between about 10 pm and 11 pm. The start of her display seems to be triggered when the light intensity around her falls below a certain level, which may explain why females in the darkness of a wood will often start glowing considerably sooner after sunset than others on nearby grassland. As well as being able to use darkness as a guide, each female is equipped with an internal 'clock'. So, for example, if a female is kept in constantly dim light with no sunset to act as a cue she will glow approximately once a day, just as she would in the wild. Strangely though, under these conditions the interval between displays is usually slightly less than the 24 hours that one might expect (in some cases her day may be as short as 17 or 18 hours), so that she starts glowing earlier and earlier each night. No one knows why this should be so, though the same effect has been noticed in other animals. During the display she may stay close to the ground, often at the base of a grass tussock, or may climb half a metre or more up a grass stem to make herself more conspicuous to searching males (Figure 17). Because the light organ is set on the underside of her body she has to twist her abdomen so that the light can be seen from above (back cover).

Glowing females can occasionally turn up in very unexpected places. During a survey in 1992 one was reported on pebbles on a beach, another had to be removed from a Post Office and two were found on a farm: one on a sheep's back and the other behind a pig's ear! One female had somehow managed to get on to an island in a pond (perhaps it had fallen in and drifted across, possibly on a bit of flotsam, or perhaps the pond had dried out at some time, allowing it to walk across).

Females sometimes seem to seek out very open areas for their displays. In old quarries, for example, they can often be found on piles of sand or gravel, several metres from the nearest vegetation, and in gardens they may choose rockeries, paving slabs or driveways, positions which would certainly make them easily spotted by passing males. At the other extreme are females which seem to hide their lights deep within bushes or among dense grass stems, where it is hard to imagine a male ever finding them.

Many species of firefly are able to switch their light on and off quite rapidly, each species producing a characteristic pattern of flashes, but our glow-worm maintains a more or less steady light. However, she will often swing her tail slowly and rhythmically from side to side, which when seen through a screen of grass can give the impression of a slow brightening and dimming. Rain does not usually put her off her glowing but on wet nights she will often display close to the ground rather than climbing a grass stem. She usually keeps up her display for two or three hours and if after that time she has not been successful in attracting a mate she will stop glowing, retreat into the grass and return for another performance the following night.

The female is extremely sedentary and can often be found night after

Figure 17. A female in a typical glowing position.

night in precisely the same spot. Moving would waste energy, which is at a premium if you are unable to eat. A few females are a bit more adventurous, though, and may wander a couple of metres between displays (this can make it rather tricky for someone who is trying to count glow-worms as it is hard to know whether the same female has reappeared or whether a new one has started to glow). It is normally only virgin females which glow: once she has mated she is unlikely to repeat her display, though if she becomes separated from her partner before they have finished mating she will often light up again immediately. Clusters of between two and six glowing females can sometimes be found within a few centimetres of each other. These clusters may well be the result of the 'ganging' of larvae mentioned earlier.

The morning after

No-one really knows where a typical female glow-worm spends her days. Even when her position is carefully marked while she is glowing at night, it is not often possible to find her again the following day. It is extremely rare to come across females above ground during the day, though one possible exception was a female which displayed from the middle of a dense patch of brambles, about half a metre above the ground. Every night she was seen on exactly the same twig, within an inch or so of the same spot, and it seems very unlikely that she could have found her way back to it night after night, through the tangle of branches, so she may have been staying there during the daytime.

Where possible the female may try

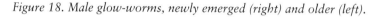

Figure 18. Male glow-worms, newly emerged (right) and older (left).

28

to escape from the light by going underground. In one of the few cases where I actually witnessed this, I watched a female one evening as she crawled down a vertical burrow about 5 mm in diameter and about 8 cm deep. It is unlikely that the female could have done the tunnelling herself, and it seems more probable that this was the abandoned burrow of a solitary bee. I found the female glow-worm, accompanied by a male, at the bottom of the tunnel the following morning. A few evenings later I spotted another female disappearing down a similar burrow. This one had a scrum of five males trying to mate with her, but as she crawled down the narrow tunnel they were all pushed off and were left wandering around trying to find her. On another site a female which had been glowing on a path was found the next day in the gap between two paving stones.

The adult male

At first glance the male glow-worm is so different in appearance from the female that it is almost hard to believe that they belong to the same species (Figure 18). Most of the external differences between the two sexes stem from the fact that the male is very much the active partner. He is the one who must do the travelling, searching for displaying females. For this reason he has well-developed wings, protected when not in use by leathery, dark brown wing cases.

Unlike ours, a male glow-worm's eyesight actually improves with age: as a larva each of his eyes would have had just one facet, but now it has more than two thousand (compared to a female's mere three hundred), allowing him to receive a much more detailed picture of his surroundings. Like the female he does not feed once

Figure 19. Male glow-worm seen from below, showing visor and large eyes.

Figure 20 (above). Decoy patterns.

Figure 21 (right). Male thorax with 'windows'.

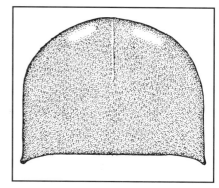

he has become an adult and so has no jaws, and like her he has the two small light-producing spots, inherited from the larva, at the tip of his abdomen, but he lacks the main light bands which are so conspicuous in the female. The male glow-worm does not generally become airborne until half an hour or more after the females begin their display, and usually finishes his search flight before many of the females have stopped glowing. If it is too windy, or if it has been raining, he may even abandon flying altogether that night. When searching for a mate the male flies within a metre or so of the ground, scanning the grass below him for the glow of a female. The upper surface of his thorax extends over the top of his head (Figure 19) and may act as a visor to protect his eyes against knocks. Although he has never seen a female before, he instinctively knows what to look for: the

Figure 22. Glow-worms mating.

Figure 23. Two males fighting over a female.

light must be of the right colour, the right brightness, the right size and the right pattern, with two bands and two dots. In one experiment males were able to distinguish between the patterns shown in Figure 20 and go for the one most resembling a female (the one on the left).

Mating

Once he has spotted a female, the male stops flying and falls to the ground. His aim is remarkable. In one experiment females were placed in glass tubes just 25 mm in diameter and yet almost two thirds of the males were able to drop straight down the neck of the tube, while the rest landed within 20 cm of the female. The male then covers the remaining short distance on foot. His visor has two clear windows, one above each eye (Figure 21), and these may enable him to see any females perching overhead.

Having reached the female he uses his sensitive antennae to feel his way on to her back and begins to mate with her (Figure 22). If they are left undisturbed mating may carry on for several hours, but it is quite common to find a female with anything from two to five males (and on very rare occasions as many as eight) jostling for position on her back (Figure 23). A challenger may attempt to prise the mating male away from the female by forcing the front edge of his thorax under that of his rival, lifting him off his feet and pushing him backwards. If this tactic fails he may crawl round to the tip of the female's abdomen and,

31

again using the front edge of his thorax, try to lever the pair apart. By repeatedly dislodging each other in this way two or more males may take it in turns to mate with the female, who often seems oblivious to the struggle taking place on her back. Her main concern, once she has attracted a mate (or several) is normally to make her way back to ground level and her daytime shelter. She may continue to glow for some time after she has started to mate, but her tail is no longer twisted over to display her light organ, so from a distance she often gives the impression that she has 'gone out'.

In fact, unlike many fireflies female glow-worms seem unable to switch off immediately, even if they are picked up and handled, and the reason may be to do with the structure of their light-organs. In the light organs of most fireflies which can flash on and off very rapidly there is usually a specialised cell, called an end-cell, at the point where each air tube meets a light-producing cell, and it has been suggested that these end-cells somehow act as taps to control the supply of oxygen to the cells. In the glow-worm's light organ these end-cells are missing, so that the air supply is connected directly to the light cells, and this may be the reason why the glow-worm takes longer to switch off. (It would be interesting to know whether the glow-worm larva, which can switch on and off several times a minute, has end-cells, but so far no-one seems to have looked for them.)

Not all glow-worms live long enough to find a mate, however. Both males and females can end up being caught by web-spinning spiders, which normally have very poor eyesight and do not seem to be put off by a meal which glows. Some females are unable to attract a male before their energy supplies run out, so their lights get weaker each night and finally go out altogether (few females can survive more than about ten nights of glowing). Ironically, celibacy appears to prolong active life, at least in glow-worms and particularly for females. Studying captive adults, Hans Schwalb found that males which had not mated lived up to three days longer than those which had. This may not sound much, but it is quite significant for an insect whose adult lifespan may only be a week. The effect was even more marked in females, in which unmated individuals lived up to ten days longer than mated ones (in fact this difference probably has more to do with the rigours of egg-laying than it does with the actual business of mating, which seems to involve very little effort, at least for the female).

The male is often the first to go. As he approaches the end of his life he becomes more and more reluctant to fly. He frequently falls onto his back, and each time he does it seems to take him longer to right himself. Finally, after an adult life of just a week or so, he dies.

Egg-laying

What the female does next depends largely upon whether she has been able to find a mate. A female which has not mated will continue to glow for as long as she can, holding on to her eggs until the last possible moment in case a male arrives, and then lays them immediately before she dies. She does not bother to arrange them, or even to stick them to a surface. These eggs do not harden as fertilised ones would, but shrivel and decay within a few weeks.

Meanwhile the female which has been able to mate behaves very differently, seeking out a suitable place in which to lay her eggs. If she chooses the wrong spot the eggs may either dry out or become waterlogged, so she uses a pair of sensitive feelers at the tip of her tail to test the surface carefully before laying.

Studies of captive glow-worms suggest that the eggs are not fully mature when the female first emerges from the pupa, so a female which attracts a male and mates on her first night as an adult must wait for a few days before the eggs are ready to be laid, whereas an older female can lay eggs almost immediately after mating.

Egg-laying normally takes just a few days. It is very rare to find an egg-laying female in the wild, but what few reports there are suggest that she lays her eggs close to the spot where she had been displaying. They appear to prefer fairly moist positions, for example under logs and stones, at the base of grass stems or in moss. The eggs may be laid singly or in clusters and each one is stuck to the surface with a film of quick-drying glue.

The number of eggs which a female can produce is roughly proportional to her size. A small female may be no more than about 12 mm in length, whereas a large one may be over 25 mm, and a clutch may vary from a couple of dozen eggs to well over 150, but a typical number is probably somewhere between 50 and 100. By the time she has finished laying her abdomen, which was once swollen with eggs, has collapsed completely and is little more than a flattened bag

Figure 24. Dead female after egg-laying.

(Figure 24. This is the same female as in Figure 22; notice the difference). She will be dead within a few days and will not see the new generation hatch to begin the next round of their extraordinary life cycle, as summarised in the figure on page 4.

Why can't females fly?

It may seem strange that female glow-worms have no wings. After all, in the ancestral firefly, from which all others evolved, both sexes were probably able to fly and at first sight it seems odd to have thrown away that ability during evolution. And yet the glow-worm is not the only species to have done so: a number of other fireflies also have flightless females (although, as far as we know, only *Phosphaenus hemipterus* has flightless males), so there must be some advantage to it. The answer may be that having evolved a light organ the female does not need to fly in order to find a male. Instead she can just flag one down with her glow. Wings cost a lot of energy to produce, and to use, and there is also a limit to how big a body they can carry, so by doing away with them the female is free to grow larger and put more of her energy into producing eggs. This theory is supported by the fact that in firefly species in which both sexes can fly they are usu-ally about the same size, whereas in species where the female is flightless she is often several times heavier than the male.

An interesting parallel occurs in moths. Here too there are species in which one sex has become flightless; again it always seems to be the female; again she has first had to develop an alternative way of calling up a mate (in this case a scent capable of drawing in males from several miles away); and again by sacrificing her flight she has been able to grow much larger than the male.

But why is it always the female that loses her wings and never the male? Firstly and most importantly, there is no real advantage in him being any larger than he already is, as he only has to produce lightweight sperm rather than heavy and energy-expensive eggs. And secondly, in virtu-ally every insect species studied so far, it is the male who is programmed to take the initiative in mating: it is he who must hunt for females, and so his wings are more important to him than the female's are to her.

Although being flightless has made good evolutionary sense to the female glow-worm for millions of years it does limit her ability to travel from site to site, and this could now have serious consequences for the survival of glow-worms as we shall see later.

Chapter 3
Distribution

Information on the glow-worm's world distribution is still very patchy, but Figure 23 gives a very rough impression of its range. This map has been produced by shading countries in which glow-worms have been seen, though of course they are unlikely to be found in every region of any country. Nevertheless it does show that 'our' glow-worm is actually an extremely widespread species, with a range stretching from Portugal and Britain in the west right across Europe and Asia to China in the east. It also survives farther north than any other firefly, almost reaching the Arctic Circle. Yet it has apparently never managed to colonise the New World, presumably because it evolved after Europe parted company with the

Americas 50–100 million years ago.

No-one knows exactly when the glow-worm first arrived in Britain. In fact it has probably had to return to this country several times, having been forced out by the harsh conditions of successive Ice Ages. After each of these, as the climate began to warm up, sea level would have been much lower than it is today and a land-bridge would have connected most of the east coast of England to the rest of Europe. Together with many other animal and plant species the glow-worm would have been able to walk across what is now the bottom of the North Sea and then to work its way across Britain. It would have been a fairly slow march, perhaps only 100 metres or so in each generation, and there

Figure 23. Approximate world distribution of glow-worms.

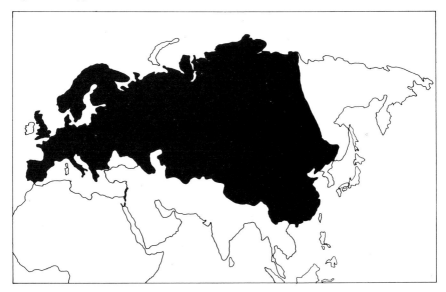

would have been countless obstacles such as rivers and mountains which would have to be skirted around, but each warm period lasted for thousands of years, giving the glow-worm plenty of time to spread into suitable habitats throughout the country.

Most of the islands around the British coast lie on a sea bed no deeper than the North Sea, so for as long as the land-bridge to Europe persisted they would have been part of the mainland, allowing glow-worms to colonise them on foot. But later, as the sea level rose, each glow-worm population would have been marooned on its own island. Ireland, on the other hand, is separated from the coasts of England and Wales by a much deeper channel, so that even in the depths of an Ice Age, when sea level was at its lowest, Ireland would have remained largely isolated from mainland Britain, though it would have been connected to the west coast of Scotland for a while. We do not know whether glow-worms have ever managed to use this bridge into Ireland after any of the earlier Ice Ages, but since the last one they have been unable to cross the Irish Sea in any numbers (there certainly seem to be plenty of suitable habitats, and from time to time there have been isolated reports of glow-worms in Ireland, but these may have been introduced).

Eventually, though, the next Ice Age would begin, forcing out all but the hardiest of species. During the past two or three million years this cycle has been repeated more than 20 times, but we cannot tell how many times glow-worms have returned to Britain.

Though glow-worms can be found in most parts of mainland Britain they are at their most abundant in southern England (Figure 24a). This may be because in this country they are at the limit of their environmental tolerance and have difficulty surviving the cooler climate further north. Certainly in both Sweden and Norway they show a very similar distribution, present in the south but absent in the north. Although they can be found on a wide range of soil types, they seem to be particularly abundant on chalk.

Glow-worms can be seen in grassland of almost every description, including downland, pastures, meadows, roadside verges, railway embankments, churchyards, golf courses and even lawns. The one type of grassy habitat which they do seem to avoid is grassland which has been 'improved' by treating it with herbicides and fertilisers. They also occur in moorland, heathland, quarries and occasionally woodland, where they are normally confined to the more open and grassy areas such as rides and clearings.

Several authors have commented that glow-worms appear to have an affinity with water, and they can often be found in reedbeds and along the banks of ponds, lakes and canals. In a survey carried out in 1992, 40 per cent of the glow-worm sites were within 100 metres of some form of open water (though of course this does not necessarily mean that they could not have survived if the water had not been there). Glow-worms may have a liking for wet sites but they are certainly not restricted to them, and many glow-worms carry on quite happily thriving on sites without any open water at all, such as chalk downland. All their habitats do have at least one thing in common, though: they generally support healthy populations of snails (Figure 24b).

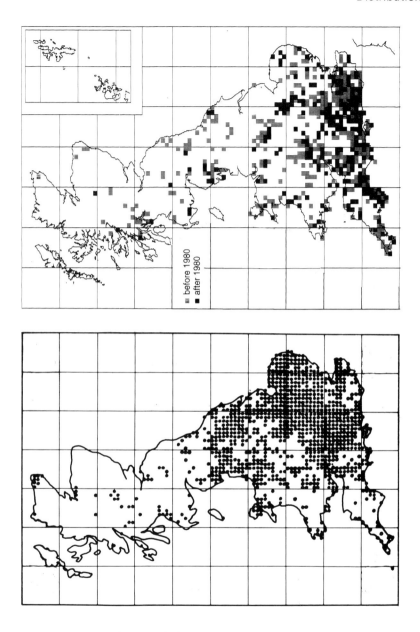

Figure 24a (top): Distribution of glow-worms, from surveys made by the Henry Doubleday Research Association, BNA (1970s) and Robin Scagell (1991–2).
Figure 24b (bottom): Distribution of non-marine molluscs, after Kerney, 1976.
Each dot represents a 10-km square with more than 40 species.

Chapter 4
A threatened species?

With such a wide distribution the immediate future of the glow-worm globally seems quite secure, but within Britain it may be less safe. Accurate statistics are hard to come by for an insect which is nocturnal and is only easy to see for a few weeks of the year, but a large body of anecdotal evidence suggests that there has been a steady fall in the British glow-worm population, certainly since the 1950s and possibly before that. Indeed they have completely vanished from many haunts where they were once common. This decline appears to be a general one, and not confined to any particular habitat or part of the country.

Although there has certainly been no shortage of suggestions as to why the glow-worm is disappearing from our countryside, there has been very little research to test any of the theories. Possible causes for the decline include:

1. Habitat destruction. There can be no doubt that many sites which once supported glow-worms have been lost through the complete destruction of their habitat. Thousands of acres of grassland have been built upon, ploughed up for arable farming, converted to conifer plantations or 'improved' using fertilisers and pesticides. So habitat destruction is certainly one factor working against glow-worms, but it cannot be the only one. There are many sites which have remained superficially unchanged for decades and yet have still lost their glow-worms.

2. Habitat fragmentation. As more and more glow-worm habitat is destroyed the surviving sites are becoming increasingly isolated from each other, separated by growing expanses of urban and arable land. Like most insects glow-worm numbers can fluctuate dramatically, often increasing or decreasing by a factor of ten or more from one year to the next, as a result of changes in food supply, predator populations, weather conditions and a host of other factors. Even without human interference these fluctuations will from time to time cause a local population to disappear altogether. A century ago, when glow-worm sites were less isolated than they are today, the gaps left by these local extinctions would soon have been filled by individuals wandering in from nearby sites. But as fragments of suitable habitat become more and more isolated this recolonisation takes longer and longer until eventually it virtually stops altogether. Then when a local population becomes extinct it stays extinct.

Glow-worms are likely to be particularly sensitive to habitat fragmentation for at least two reasons. First, being predators they tend to occur in smaller numbers than their prey, and so may be more susceptible to local extinctions. Second, as we have already seen, although the male is relatively mobile the wingless female is almost completely sedentary throughout her adult life. So the glow-worm's ability to colonise new sites, or to recolonise vacated ones, is limited by how far the female larva can travel on foot. A river, a ploughed field or even a busy road can pose quite a formidable barrier and will reduce the chances of an empty site being repopulated.

It is interesting to note here that had the roles been reversed, with the male being the flightless sex, then this situation would not have been quite so serious. To establish a new colony a winged female from a nearby population could simply have mated with a male on her own site, flown to the new site and laid eggs there. As it is, with the female wingless, a female larva must walk, rather than fly, to the new site and then somehow find either a male which has flown there or one which has also walked there as a larva and then pupated. The chances of this happening seem slim for all but the closest of sites.

3. Pollution. There is another reason why being a predator may put the glow-worm in a vulnerable position. Being at the top of a food chain it is likely to absorb any pollutants eaten by the snails on which it feeds. Pesticide and herbicide sprays drifting from nearby fields or industrial chemicals washed from the air by rain become concentrated as they pass up the food chain from plant to snail to glow-worm, where they may accumulate. Many pesticides are particularly soluble in fat and since the larva's main role in life is to stockpile the food reserves which it will need as an adult most of its body is packed with globules of fat. Compounds which were originally too dilute to kill either the plants or the snails may build up in these fat-bodies, to be released when the fat reserves are drawn upon by the

pupa and the adult. This may kill the glow-worm outright or simply lower its fitness, for example by reducing the number or viability of the eggs it lays.

4. Distraction by artificial lights. Male glow-worms are normally very precise in distinguishing between females of their own species and other light sources, but they are sometimes drawn to house lights or street lamps. It may be that they treat an artificial light not as a female glow-worm but as the moon or stars and, in trying to navigate by it, spiral in towards it just as moths do. It is quite possible that on sites close to bright artificial lights males either become distracted by them or find it difficult to spot females in the glare, but we do not yet know how important a factor this is in the overall fall in glow-worm numbers. The glow-worm sites reported in the 1992 survey tended to be well away from any form of artificial lighting. On the other hand a few females were found displaying directly under streetlights, but we do not know whether this prevented them from attracting males.

5. Insufficient grazing. Most of the grassland in Britain was originally created by clearing forests to make way for farming, but left unmanaged trees soon begin to move in and the grassland reverts first to scrub and then to woodland. Prior to this century the invasion of grassland by trees was largely held in check by grazing animals, particularly sheep and rabbits. But within the last century many sheep farmers have abandoned the unimproved and unmanaged downland slopes which once provided one of the richest habitats for glow-worms, preferring instead the flatter, 'improved' fields of the valleys.

The impact of this decline in sheep grazing on downland habitats was compounded in 1953 by the introduction of the myxomatosis virus. Within the first few years it had killed an estimated 99 per cent of the rabbits in Britain, and although with time rabbits have become more resistant, their population in many areas is still just a fraction of that immediately before myxomatosis. Less grazing means longer grass and more scrub, conditions which have proved intolerable for a number of grassland plants and animals, including several orchids, the wheatear and the large blue butterfly (which disappeared from this country in 1979). The glow-worm may be another victim of scrub invasion, in which case it may be possible to slow its decline, at least locally, by reintroducing sheep grazing to selected grassland habitats.

6. **Changes in climate.** There has been growing concern recently over the possible consequences of the 'greenhouse effect', in which the burning of fossil fuels leads to a build-up of carbon dioxide in the atmosphere. This may reduce the amount of heat radiating back into space, leading to global warming, which in turn could have secondary effects such as changes in rainfall and other weather patterns. Detecting these changes against the background of an already variable climate is extremely difficult and open to a variety of interpretations, so as yet there is still very little agreement as to whether the burning of fossil fuels has actually affected our climate and, if so, to what extent and for how long. These questions will have to be answered before a link between global warming and the disappearance of glow-worms can be suggested, but it is certainly a possibility.

A lot more research will be needed before the cause, or causes, of the glow-worm's gradual decline is known, and only then can we look for ways of halting it. In the next chapter we will look in more detail at some of the questions which will need to be answered.

Chapter 5
What don't we know?

As with most things, what we do know about glow-worms is dwarfed by what we have yet to find out about them. The list of questions awaiting an answer is endless, and each question is likely to involve answering several others, but the following would make a good starting point.

1. How widespread is the glow-worm's decline? Are its numbers dwindling throughout the world or just in particular regions or countries? Information is scarce at the moment but in Denmark, for example, glow-worms were very common at the beginning of the 20th century but are now restricted to a handful of sites. Naturalists in Sweden and Switzerland have noticed a similar fall in numbers. How long has the decline been going on, and are all habitats equally affected? To answer these questions it will be necessary to monitor glow-worm populations on a large number of sites over a period of many years.

2. How important is habitat fragmentation in the disappearance of glow-worms? To tackle this question we would have to follow population changes on a large number of sites varying in size and the degree of isolation from other glow-worm populations. If habitat fragmentation is one of the reasons for glow-worms disappearing from some sites then we would expect small, isolated sites to be most at risk.

3. What effect is pollution having on glow-worms? To study this we need to measure the concentrations of substances such as pesticides and other man-made compounds in the tissues of glow-worms living on a wide range of sites and to relate these concentrations to any long-term changes in the glow-worm population of each site, making allowance for any other factors.

4. To what extent are males distracted by, or attracted to, artificial lights? Do some types of light cause more disturbance than others and over what sort of distance will they draw males? This question could be studied either by watching the response of individual males (either captive or wild) to a range of different lights, or by looking for changes in glow-worm numbers on sites where lights have been installed nearby.

5. Are glow-worms affected by changes in grazing? Here we would need to look at the abundance of glow-worms in fields grazed by different species (such as rabbits, sheep or cattle) and at different intensities. For example one count, at Aston Rowant National Nature Reserve, Oxfordshire, recorded more than twice as many glowing females in an area of grassland grazed at two sheep per acre as in a corresponding area grazed at six sheep per acre. The total number of glow-worms counted was just 48, making it far too small a sample to draw any firm conclusions, but it does suggest that too much grazing (or grazing by the wrong species) may be as harmful as too little.

6. Has a change in the climate contributed to the fall in glow-worm numbers? This will be one of the most difficult questions to answer and will have to wait until we have a much better understanding of how our climate works and how it has changed.

7. It often appears that the female glow-worms emerge a few days earlier than the males, but is this really true? So far relatively little is known about males in the wild because it is normally very difficult to find them until they have arrived at a female, so any males emerging before the first females would go unnoticed. Recently, however, Malcolm Jennings has developed an ingenious 'battery-operated female' which uses a light-emitting diode to imitate the real thing. So effective is this mimicry that in one instance two males which had begun to mate with a female immediately abandoned her and went over to the battery-operated version! Devices of this sort should make it easier to study males without having to rely on females to attract them.

8. What is the average lifespan of a male glow-worm in the wild?

9. Does the male mate just with the first female that he finds, or does he then go on to look for others? In a study at Sevenoaks Reserve 32 males were collected from females, marked with white ink or typist's correction fluid and released in the same place. Not one of them was caught again, even though there were often other females still glowing just a few inches away. It may be that not enough males were marked, or it may suggest that each male normally only mates with one female. Many more studies will be needed to be sure.

10. How important are weather conditions to glowing females and flying males? Males seem to be put off flying by strong winds and low temperatures, and females tend to huddle low in the grass on wet nights, which might make them more difficult to spot from the air. This factor could be particularly important if our climate is indeed changing.

11. How far will a typical male fly in search of females? Again the battery-operated females should help in answering this question. By using several of them, spaced at different distances, and by marking any males that they attract, it should be possible to discover how far (and how fast) a male can fly. The shorter the male's range the more difficult it is likely to be to recolonise lost sites, and the more inbreeding there will be within each glow-worm population.

12. What is the range of a glow-worm larva? Can it survive in apparently inhospitable habitats such as arable fields? This too will determine how readily a new or lost site can be recolonised.

13. What are the larva's food preferences in the wild? In captivity they will tackle virtually any type of snail they are given, but might they be more selective in the wild? The only way to find out would be by patiently watching wild larvae.

14. How feasible would it be to reintroduce glow-worms to sites where they have become extinct? Restocking might be possible on sites where they have disappeared through natural fluctuations in their numbers, but it is less likely to work where the habitat has been damaged, for example by pollution. How many individuals are needed to stand a reasonable chance of becoming established, and at what stage in their life cycle should they be introduced? This will depend on which stage is the most vulnerable in the wild: if, for example, predators eating the eggs account for the most glow-worm deaths then it would be better to hatch them in captivity and release the young larvae. So far very few attempts have been made to introduce glow-worms to new areas, but at least one has been successful: 119 larvae, hatched from the eggs of a single female, were released on to an area of grass at Sevenoaks in 1988 and by 1993 they had established a small breeding colony.

15. What are the glow-worm's habitat requirements? Even on a site which supports a healthy glow-worm colony they are often restricted to one particular area. By measuring as many environmental conditions as possible, in areas both with and without glow-worms, it may be possible to find out how sensitive they are to factors such as temperature, frost, artificial lighting and the type of vegetation. For example, the 1992 survey mentioned earlier seemed to suggest that glow-worms may prefer south and west-facing sites to north and east-facing ones, but many more records will be needed to check this.

16. Is it possible to manage habitats so as to encourage glow-worms? A small-scale study at Sevenoaks for example suggests that it may be possible to create a better habitat for them by cutting the grass at least once during the summer. By looking at the numbers of glow-worms in habitats managed in different ways (for example by scrub clearance, grazing, mowing or even burning) we may be able to find the glow-worm's 'ideal' habitat. For example, it is probably not a good idea to use chemicals on the site, particularly those likely to affect the snail population.

Only by finding answers to at least some of these questions will it be possible to tackle what are perhaps the most urgent and yet most difficult questions: why are glow-worms disappearing, and how can this decline be halted?

Some of the questions will require a lot of detailed research involving a lot of technical apparatus, but many could be tackled by anyone with enough time, patience and enthusiasm. At the same time it is obviously essential that we do not cause any unnecessary disturbance to the glow-worms that we are studying, otherwise we will simply be adding to the problems which they already face.

Breeding glow-worms

I have often been asked whether it is possible to introduce glow-worms on to a site, particularly into a garden, but there are several problems with this idea. Taking large numbers of glow-worms from an existing colony to start a new one could just make matters worse for the original population, which might already be struggling to survive. It is possible to breed and rear glow-worms in captivity, to be released on to a new site, but it is a very difficult and time-consuming process to hatch the eggs and house the larvae in a suitable environment for two years or more, keeping up a constant supply of live snails.

Then there is the question of whether the new site will provide a suitable habitat for glow-worms. On many existing sites the glow-worms are confined to one patch, completely ignoring other areas of apparently identical habitat. The site must also be large enough to support a viable population, and may require regular management such as mowing, grazing or scrub clearance.

In short, although introducing glow-worms on to new sites, or reintroducing them on to abandoned ones, may become an essential part of conserving them, at the moment very little is known about its feasibility. It is best done as part of an organised project, with proper planning, involvement of the relevant conservation bodies, appropriate habitat management and long-term monitoring of the new population. It should certainly not be used simply as a way of making a garden more interesting, or keeping down the snails; it is far better to find an established colony in your area and go to them rather than trying to force them to come to you.

Some glow-worm sites

A complete list of glow-worm sites cannot be given, since there are hundreds of sites across the country, many of which are on private property. The distribution map on page 37 shows the areas where they are abundant. There are, however, a number of locations where glow-worms can be found reliably year after year. A short selection is given below. Please treat the glow-worms and the sites with care: be careful where you are treading in the dark.

South-West Peninsula: on many coast paths, notably around Thurlestone and Slapton Ley, Devon. Also on roadside by Earth Station at Goonhilly, Cornwall.

Chilterns: on many, possibly most, areas of chalk downland. Large numbers on Aston Rowant Nature Reserve near Stokenchurch.

South Downs: on some open downland, such as The Trundle near Chichester.

Kent: along numerous hedgerows; also at Firehills near Hastings.

Central England: large numbers can be seen some years at Barnack Hills and Holes, Cambridgeshire.

Cheshire: along canals near Bunbury; along Middlewood Way near Bollington.

Lancashire: reported from either side of the Kent estuary.

Wales and Lakes: by streams in valley floors, though only in small numbers.

Scotland: scarce; one or two sites around Appin, Argyllshire, and on loch banks.

Chapter 6
Glow-worm watching

No amount of words or photographs can replace the experience of seeing glow-worms for yourself. The earlier chapters of this book should give you some idea of when and where to find them, but here is a summary.

When?

The glow-worm season varies considerably from one site to another, and from one year to the next on the same site but in general the best time to look for them is between mid-June and mid-July. Even during the season there will be odd nights when there happen to be no females about (for example if they all succeeded in attracting a male the previous night), so do not give up if you fail to see any on the first visit. They can be seen most clearly on a moonless or overcast night. The females normally begin their display between about 10 pm and 11 pm, and few carry on much beyond midnight. As a rough guide it is worth waiting until your eyes can no longer make out colours in your surroundings before beginning your search. Outside the breeding season glowing larvae can still be found occasionally, though their dim lights make them much harder to find than the females.

Where?

Glow-worms can be found in most parts of the country, though they do appear to be more common in southern Britain than in the north. It is worth looking for them on almost any area of unimproved grassland, but the best sites of all are on downland which is unploughed and unsprayed. Other habitats which often support glow-worms include canal towpaths, grass verges, gardens, heathland, moorland, old quarries, woodland rides and clearings, river banks, lake margins, churchyards and clifftops. In urban and suburban areas one of the most promising places to search is on a disused railway line. These act as 'biological corridors', unbroken strands of habitat which stretch for miles and allow glow-worms (and many other animals and plants) from the surrounding countryside to penetrate right into the centre of a town. You can often save yourself a lot of fruitless searching simply by contacting your County Trust for Nature Conservation, who will probably be able to point you towards a nearby nature reserve where glow-worms have been seen. It is probably best to start with a known glow-worm site before looking for new ones.

Despite the brilliance of the glow-worm's light it can easily be swamped by the beam of a bright torch, especially if the female is glowing deep inside a bush or a tussock of grass, so it is often better to familiarise yourself with the site first during the day and then rely on natural light when searching. Females do not seem to be particularly disturbed by torchlight and once you have found one she will usually continue to glow while you take a closer look at her.

National surveys have been carried

out for several years, with the aid of hundreds of members of the public who have heard about them through radio broadcasts, magazine articles or even by word of mouth. The aim is to build up a picture of the distribution of glow-worms, and how it varies from year to year. It is becoming clear that numbers do fluctuate considerably from site to site, and even from night to night – on one occasion in 1993, for example, Robin Scagell recorded 230 glowing females during a standard half-hour walk on one night, and only five the next, following a sudden cold snap. By collecting and collating such information it may eventually be possible to find some of the factors which affect glow-worm numbers.

We are always interested to hear of new sites, or to receive more details of known sites (if you prefer your records to be treated in confidence then we will not publish details of them without your permission). Please include the following details: Ordnance Survey grid reference (most important); name of nearest town or village; county; type of site (garden, nature reserve etc); habitats; dates and numbers of glow-worms seen. Alternatively, you might like to photocopy the standard survey form on the facing page. Any notes about interesting behaviour are particularly welcome. Please send any records to:

John Tyler, Sevenoaks Reserve, Bradbourne Vale Road, Sevenoaks, Kent TN13 3DH.

Photography

The one essential piece of equipment for photographing a glowing female is a camera which has the facility to leave the shutter open for long periods. To avoid vibration the camera will need to be mounted on a tripod (with some models it is possible to reverse the central column of the tripod so that the camera is suspended between the legs, allowing you to get it much closer to the ground) and operated with a cable release. You may need to use a torch so that you have enough light to focus by. The time for which the shutter has to be left open will of course depend on which film and which lens you are using, but as a rough guide it is probably best to take a series of photographs, starting with an exposure of about a second and roughly doubling the time with each picture, up to about two minutes. Using extension rings or a macro lens in addition to your standard lens will of course increase the exposure time.

Choosing the right female is quite important. A female glowing partway up a grass stem is likely to give a clearer, less cluttered picture than one on the ground, but may sway about in the slightest breeze, so it may be worth waiting for an absolutely still night or improvising some form of wind-break. Some females will remain perfectly motionless, but many have the unfortunate habit of slowly waving their abdomens from side to side. If this happens while taking a picture it is usually possible to avoid getting a smudged image simply by placing your hand in front of the lens until she has stopped moving.

If you are using a manual aperture setting it is probably best to have the lens fully open (i.e. the lowest F number). Although this gives a relatively shallow depth of field, making it fairly critical to get the glow-worm correctly focused, it does keep the exposure

Glow-worm Survey Form

Your name

Your address

Name of site   **County**

Ordnance Survey Grid Reference *(two letters and six numbers)*

For new sites, please draw a sketch map overleaf showing the location of the site in relation to roads, railways and other nearby landmarks, and show the area which you have searched (either the boundary of the area or the path which you walked). Please also mark the approximate position of the glow worms and give an idea of the scale.

Details of visits

				Females (glowing)	**Number of** Males (on females)	Larvae
Visit	Date	Time	Conditions*			
1						
2						
3						
4						
5						
6						
7						
8						

(continue on a separate sheet if necessary)

Type of site (please tick): Nature Reserve ☐ Garden ☐   Roadside ☐   Railway ☐
          Waterside ☐   Sea cliff ☐   Quarry ☐   Grassland ☐   Other ☐

Position of glow worms *(tick more than one if necessary)*:
Short grass ☐ Long grass ☐ Under trees ☐ In hedge ☐ On path ☐ On gravel or stones☐ Other ☐

Is there any permanent open water within 100 metres of the glow worms?
No ☐ Stream or ditch ☐ Pond ☐   Lake ☐   River ☐   Canal ☐   Sea ☐

Are you aware of any chemicals used on the land?
Definitely not ☐ Yes – weedkillers ☐   Yes – insecticides ☐   Yes – slug pellets ☐   Don't know☐

Is the area grazed? No ☐ Sheep ☐ Cattle☐ Horses ☐   Rabbits ☐   Deer ☐

Is there a slope or open aspect to the site? No Yes – N NE E SE S SW W NW

Artificial lighting   None☐ Distant lights – over 200 metres ☐ 50-200 metres ☐
          Bright lights nearby ☐ House lights only ☐   Lights from passing traffic ☐

Any other comments about the site
(eg early records of glow worms not previously reported, changes in use of the site either in the past or planned)

Please return this form to John Tyler, Tadorna, Bradbourne Vale Road, Sevenoaks, Kent TN13 3DH

*Choose from: Dry, Raining, Wet ground (ie droplets on vegetation), Windy. Also give night time temperature if you can.

time to a minimum, thus reducing the risk of the picture becoming blurred by movement. Finally, you might like to experiment with the use of a flash during the exposure to bring out the shape of the female and her surroundings. A similar effect can be achieved by sweeping a torch beam over the background, though this tends to give the photograph a rather unnatural orange tinge.

Domestic camcorders are more sensitive to light than most cameras, and it is quite easy to video glow-worms with a modern camera with a sensitivity of 5 lux or better and a good macro facility. However, the same problems will be encountered as with conventional photography – if the glow-worm is too small within the frame the result will be small, uninspiring green dots. Some additional light is needed, and a torch is perfectly adequate. Camcorders can usually compensate for the redder colour of torchlight compared with daylight, so the results can look very natural.

Finding glow-worms may require a little time and patience, but the reward is certainly well worth the effort.

Bibliography

Balduf, W. (1935) *Bionomics of entomophagous coleoptera.* Swift.

Blair, K.G. (1927). An aquatic Lampyrid larva from S. Celebes. *Trans. Ent. Soc., London,* **75**, 43–5.

British Naturalists' Association (1971). Glow-worm Survey. *Country-Side,* **21** (10), 457–63, 572–4.

British Naturalists' Association (1974). Glow-worm Survey. *Country-Side,* **22** (6), 266–71.

Dreisig, H. (1971). Control of the glowing of *Lampyris noctiluca* in the field. *J. Zool., London,* **165**, 229–44.

Dreisig, H. (1974). Observations on the luminescence of the larval glow worm, *Lampyris noctiluca. Ent. Scand.,* **5**, 103–9.

Dreisig, H. (1978). The circadian rhythm of bioluminescence in the glow worm, *Lampyris noctiluca. Behav. Ecol. Sociobiol.,* **3**, 1–18.

Linssen, E.F. (1959). *Beetles of the British Isles.* Warne.

Lloyd, J.E. (1971). Bioluminescent communication in insects. *Annu. Rev. Entomol.,* **16**, 97–122.

McDermott, F.A., The taxonomy of the Lampyridae (Coleoptera). *Trans. Amer. Ent. Soc.,* **90**, 1–72.

Schwalb, H.H. (1961). Beitrage zur biologie der einheimischen Lampyriden *Lampyris noctiluca* und *Phausis splendidula* und experimentella analyse ihres beutefang- and sexualverhaltens. *Zool. Jb. Syst.,* **88**, 399–550.

Tyler, J. (1986). The ecology and conservation of the glow-worm, *Lampyris noctiluca* (L.) in Britain. *Atala,* **10–12**, 17–19.

Vogel, R. (1913). The topography and development of the luminescent organs of *Lampyris noctiluca. Zool. Anz.,* **41**, 325–32.

Wigglesworth, V.B. (1972). *Principles of insect physiology.* Chapman & Hall.

Wootton, A. (1976). Rearing the glow worm (*Lampyris noctiluca* L.). *Entomologist's Record,* **88**, 64–7.